READING POWER PLUS

100 Worksheets for a Reading Skills Workout
Grades 1–6

by Nicholas P. Criscuolo, Susan R. Fineman,
and Adrienne P. McCarthy

Fearon Teacher Aids
a division of
David S. Lake Publishers
Belmont, California

Editorial director: Ina Tabibian
Development editor: Emily Hutchinson
Production editor: Stephen Feinstein
Design director: Eleanor Mennick
Designer: Colleen Forbes
Illustrator: Christian H. Dutsch
Compositor: Pamela Cattich
Manufacturing manager: Casimira Kostecki

ISBN 0-8224-5812-8

Printed in the United States of America

1. 9 8 7 6 5 4 3 2 1

Contents

Animal Crackers

Read down to find each animal's name in the cage. Circle it. Then check it off in the box below.

```
b  s  o  r  l  s  z  m  b  s
e  e  g  t  l  n  o  b  l  l
a  a  i  l  v  a  n  i  r  r
z  l  r  l  t  b  k  r  b  m
e  t  a  a  i  t  s  d  e  o
b  i  f  m  g  l  n  g  a  n
r  g  f  a  e  i  a  i  r  k
a  r  e  s  r  o  k  f  l  e
t  y  n  e  b  n  e  f  o  y
```

seal	llama	snake
bear	zebra	bird
monkey	tiger	lion
giraffe		

Skill: finding hidden words

Name _____

Countdown

Ten space travel words are hidden on the rocket. They are written either ——→ or ↓ . Circle them and write them in the blanks in any order you like.

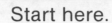

Start here.

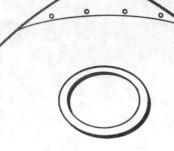

```
a  o  b  c  l  v  w  y  n  o
s  r  o  c  k  e  t  x  m  e
w  b  d  l  e  a  r  y  o  a
v  i  s  p  a  c  e  s  o  p
u  t  s  o  s  t  u  u  n  c
s  p  t  o  d  h  n  n  n  o
p  l  a  n  e  t  c  v  e  m
v  a  r  g  a  l  a  x  y  e
b  a  s  t  r  o  n  a  u  t
```

10. _____

9. _____

8. _____

7. _____

6. _____

5. _____

4. _____

3. _____

2. _____

1. _____

Blastoff!

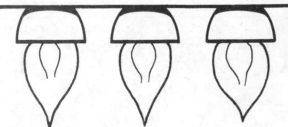

Skill: finding hidden words   2

Reading Power Plus, © 1986 David S. Lake Publishers

What's in a Word?

Each of these words has at least one smaller word hidden in it. Find one hidden word of three letters or more in each word below and write it in the blank.

1. plane _____
2. grow _____
3. howl _____
4. cart _____
5. star _____
6. hotel _____
7. money _____
8. crack _____
9. spool _____
10. below _____

11. cloud _____
12. monkey _____
13. paste _____
14. scar _____
15. elephant _____
16. train _____
17. toil _____
18. floats _____
19. spoke _____
20. waste _____

Reading Power Plus, © 1986 David S. Lake Publishers

Skill: finding hidden words

Which Is Which?

Beside each sentence are two words that sound alike but are spelled differently. Choose the word that completes the sentence correctly. Write it in the blank.

here	hear	1. Do you _____ a noise?
hour	our	2. That is _____ house.
pear	pair	3. Do you want a peach or a _____?
stare	stair	4. It is not polite to _____.
see	sea	5. Can you _____ the ocean from here?
new	knew	6. Everyone _____ Jo was shy.
do	due	7. Your book is _____ at the library.
hoarse	horse	8. Lee was _____ and her throat hurt.
fir	fur	9. We have a _____ tree in our yard.
seem	seam	10. The _____ in my coat is torn.
too	two	11. The tailor made the pants _____ long.
be	bee	12. The _____ went from flower to flower.
hair	hare	13. Her long red _____ was turning gray.
days	daze	14. There are seven _____ in a week.
ring	wring	15. I will _____ out this wet towel.

Skill: using homonyms

4

A Pair of Pears

Read each pair of clues. Write each answer in the blanks on the pears. (Both answers for each box sound the same but are spelled differently.)

1. One and one	**a.** Another word for **also**
2. A daughter and a _____	**b.** It shines during the day.
3. It's like a rabbit.	**c.** It grows on your head.
4. The color of the sky	**d.** She _____ out the candle.
5. A dogs wags it.	**e.** A story
6. We make bread with it.	**f.** A rose, a daisy, or a tulip

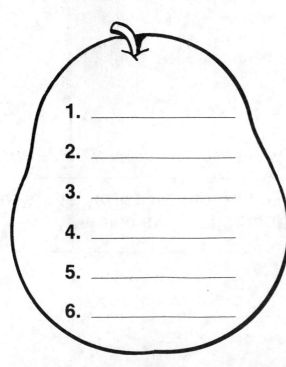

1. _____
2. _____
3. _____
4. _____
5. _____
6. _____

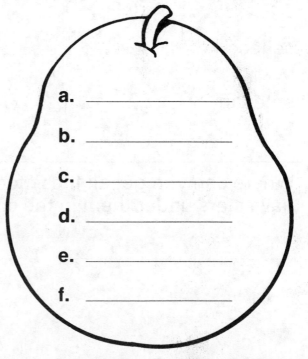

a. _____
b. _____
c. _____
d. _____
e. _____
f. _____

Skill: using homonyms

Food for Thought

Rearrange the letters to spell the name of a food.

1. inonos   ___ ___ ___ ___ ___ ___
                                   ☆

2. posu   ___ ___ ___ ___
                ☆

3. sepgra   ___ ___ ___ ___ ___ ___
                   ☆

4. hikecnc   ___ ___ ___ ___ ___ ___ ___
                           ☆

5. dabre   ___ ___ ___ ___ ___
           ☆

6. klmi   ___ ___ ___ ___
    ☆

7. toptaoes   ___ ___ ___ ___ ___ ___ ___ ___
              ☆

8. rkutye   ___ ___ ___ ___ ___ ___
        ☆

9. klcipse   ___ ___ ___ ___ ___ ___ ___
            ☆

10. sehece   ___ ___ ___ ___ ___ ___
        ☆

11. sutepan   ___ ___ ___ ___ ___ ___ ___
              ☆

_____

12. Where can you get all these foods? To find out, write the letters that have stars under them in the corresponding blanks below.

___ ___ ___ ___ ___ ___ ___ ___ ___ ___ ___
 1   2   3   4   5   6   7   8   9 10 11

Make the Connection

Read each incomplete sentence. Choose the word that best completes it. Write the word in the blank.

1. **Tell** is to **told** as **sell** is to _____ .
   bell   sold   buy   give

2. **Snow** is to **cold** as **fire** is to _____ .
   flame   cook   camp   hot

3. **Geese** is to **goose** as **feet** is to _____ .
   foot   shoe   toe   sock

4. **Tub** is to **but** as **ton** is to _____ .
   box   not   nut   big

5. **Spider** is to **web** as **bird** is to _____ .
   wing   fly   egg   nest

6. **Simple** is to **easy** as **big** is to _____ .
   fresh   large   clever   good

7. **Rice** is to **ice** as **grow** is to _____ .
   row   now   cold   water

8. **Horn** is to **honk** as **clock** is to _____ .
   hour   tick   time   clown

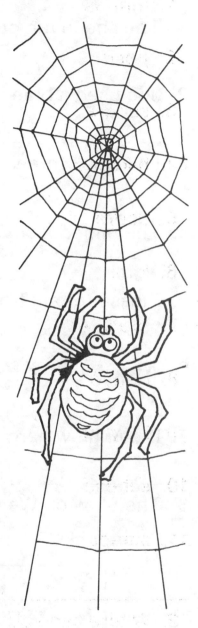

Skill: completing analogies

Match Maker

From the box below, choose the correct definition for each underlined word. Write it in the blank.

1. The sheep ran out when the <u>pen</u> was opened.

   _____

2. Joe used a blue <u>pen</u> to write his name.

   _____

3. I will <u>pick</u> three people for my team.

   _____

4. The miner used a <u>pick</u> to dig out the coal.

   _____

5. Please <u>refrain</u> from eating too much candy.

   _____

6. We sang the <u>refrain</u>, but only Nan knew the entire song.

   _____

7. If you <u>blow</u> hard, all the candles will go out.

   _____

8. The <u>blow</u> on Wendy's head knocked her out.

   _____

pen	• an instrument used for writing • a place to keep animals
pick	• to choose • a tool used for breaking soil
refrain	• a verse repeated in music • to keep oneself back
blow	• to expel air from the mouth • a sudden hard stroke or hit

Reading Power Plus, © 1986 David S. Lake Publishers

Look-Alikes

Choose the correct definition for each underlined word. Write the letter of the definition in the blank.

_____

_____ 1. At the picnic, Heather drank <u>punch</u>.

_____ 2. The boxer took a <u>punch</u> in the nose.

    a. fruit juice   **b.** a hit with a fist

_____ 3. If you are tired, you can <u>rest</u> on my bed.

_____ 4. The bed is made, but the <u>rest</u> of the room is a mess.

    a. that which is left   **b.** to lie down, to be still

_____ 5. The woman was sick and needed to <u>fast</u> for a day.

_____ 6. The child was able to walk <u>fast</u>, even though her leg was in a cast.

    a. quickly   **b.** to stop eating

_____ 7. Tony tried to <u>jam</u> his clothes into the drawer.

_____ 8. Dee likes strawberry <u>jam</u> on wheat toast.

    a. a sweet food   **b.** to squeeze into a tight position

_____ 9. Even though the screen was closed, a <u>fly</u> got into the room.

_____ 10. Do you ever wish you could <u>fly</u> like a bird?

    a. an insect that has wings   **b.** to move through the air

Skill: understanding homographs

Double Trouble

Write the letter of the correct definition above each underlined word.

1. If Jane <u>bows</u> too low after the show, the <u>bows</u> will fall out of her hair.
   a. ribbons tied in loops
   b. bends forward and lowers the head

2. Do not <u>wind</u> up the string in the <u>wind</u>.
   a. air in motion
   b. to roll into a ball

3. The <u>tear</u> in her dress caused a <u>tear</u> in her eye.
   a. a rip
   b. a drop of liquid

4. The car that will <u>lead</u> the parade uses gas without <u>lead</u>.
   a. a soft, bluish-gray metal
   b. to go first

5. Please <u>record</u> the names of everyone who listens to that <u>record</u>.
   a. a round, flat disk for reproducing sound
   b. to set down in writing

6. It will take more than a <u>minute</u> to sort these <u>minute</u> stones.
   a. 60 seconds
   b. tiny

7. Will anyone <u>object</u> if we use a sharp <u>object</u> on stage?
   a. a thing that can be seen and touched
   b. to protest

Reading Power Plus, © 1986 David S. Lake Publishers

Pay Attention!

If the words in each pair have the same meaning, write **S** in the blank. If the words have opposite meanings, write **a** in the blank.

_____	1. open	close	_____	11. smash	break
_____	2. spin	turn	_____	12. sound	noise
_____	3. low	high	_____	13. clear	cloudy
_____	4. short	long	_____	14. smile	frown
_____	5. over	under	_____	15. auto	car
_____	6. inside	outside	_____	16. sofa	couch
_____	7. begin	end	_____	17. plain	fancy
_____	8. tug	pull	_____	18. house	home
_____	9. loud	soft	_____	19. every	each
_____	10. gift	present	_____	20. quiet	still

Skill: recognizing synonyms and antonyms

Name _____

It's Not All the Same

If the underlined words mean the same, write **same** in the blank. If they mean the opposite, write **opposite.**

1. I will <u>inquire</u> about my missing glove.
   Will you <u>answer</u> the child's difficult question?   _____

2. The dinosaur <u>exhibit</u> is very popular.
   The window <u>display</u> drew a large crowd.   _____

3. Chris's worst <u>habit</u> is cracking her knuckles.
   Our <u>custom</u> is to have fruit after dinner.   _____

4. The orders <u>include</u> milk and cereal.
   Ted must <u>exclude</u> chocolate from his diet.   _____

5. The reckless driver <u>survived</u> the crash.
   Lynne cried when her dog <u>perished</u> in the fire.   _____

6. The fog <u>disappeared</u> by noon.
   The thief <u>vanished</u> in the night.   _____

7. The florist had a large <u>assortment</u> of plants.
   Plant a <u>variety</u> of vegetables.   _____

Skill: recognizing synonyms and antonyms   16

Reading Power Plus, © 1986 David S. Lake Publishers

Pick and Choose

Find the two words in the box below that best answer each riddle.
Write them in the blanks.

1. You do these with your nose.

   _____   _____

2. These grow in dirt.

   _____   _____

3. These may be found in a nest.

   _____   _____

4. These have wheels.

   _____   _____

5. You buy these in bakeries.

   _____   _____

6. You learn to do these in school.

   _____   _____

7. These are more than five.

   _____   _____

8. A puppy is both of these things.

   _____   _____

smell	taxi	flowers	cookies
eggs	pet	chicks	dog
read	sniff	bread	truck
nine	seven	spell	weeds

Skill: extending word meanings

Picnic Puzzle

Read the clues. Write the answers in the puzzle.

ACROSS
 1 A fruit whose name rhymes with **each**
 4 A sweet treat
 5 A dessert with filling and crust
 7 Something you chew but do not swallow
 9 A birthday ____ has candles on top.
 10 A round toy for throwing

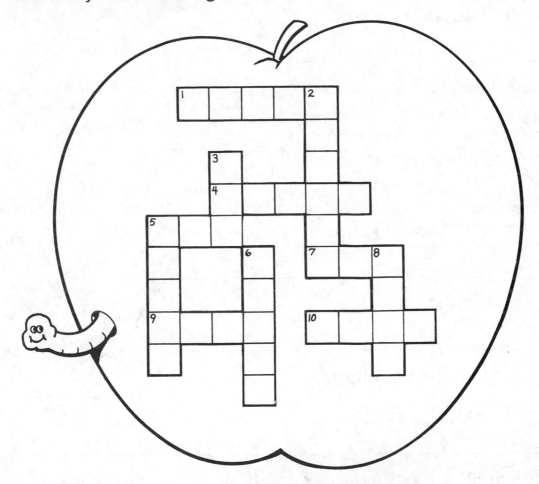

DOWN
 2 You eat it with a long bun and mustard.
 3 Frozen water
 5 A drink made from fruit
 6 The color of grass
 8 A white drink

Reading Power Plus, © 1986 David S. Lake Publishers

What Does It Mean?

Draw a line under the correct answer for each question.

What does it mean if—

1. a boat **capsizes?**

   It overturns.   It loses its sail.

2. a boy is **cranky?**

   He is grouchy.   He needs a bath.

3. the roof **collapses?**

   It falls in.   It catches on fire.

4. a bottle **shatters?**

   It loses its label.   It breaks.

5. an ankle **swells?**

   It gets bigger.   It is dirty.

6. a plan is **cancelled?**

   It is good.   It is not to be used.

7. a girl feels **clumsy?**

   She feels lonely.   She feels awkward.

8. a tooth **decays?**

   It rots.   It is crooked.

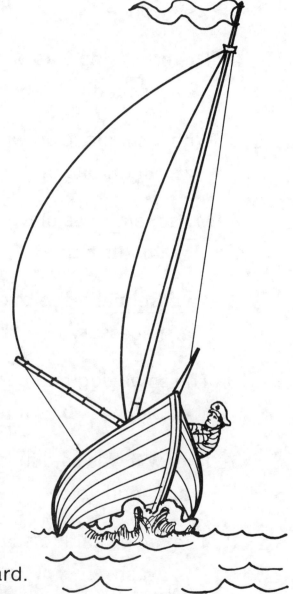

Skill: extending word meanings

Easy As A, B, C

Find the meaning of the underlined word in each sentence. Write the letter in the blank.

_____ 1. No one understood the <u>cryptic</u> message on the wall.

    a. wonderful   **b.** mysterious   **c.** well-written

_____ 2. The cruel king was <u>banished</u> from the country.

    a. rescued   **b.** hidden   **c.** sent away

_____ 3. With his knife, Don <u>whittled</u> the wood into a toy.

    a. cut off bits of   **b.** folded   **c.** painted

_____ 4. My <u>scheme</u> was clever, but it would be hard to explain.

    a. middle name   **b.** sister   **c.** plan of action

_____ 5. An <u>essential</u> piece of camping equipment is a flashlight.

    a. necessary   **b.** enjoyable   **c.** extra

_____ 6. The small dog had become <u>pudgy</u> after years of overeating.

    a. old   **b.** wild   **c.** chubby

_____ 7. I know it was said in <u>jest</u>, but it hurt my feelings.

    a. a loud voice   **b.** a joking way   **c.** a hallway

_____ 8. The recipe said to <u>scald</u> milk in a saucepan.

    a. wash   **b.** cool   **c.** heat

Skill: extending word meanings

Mystery Months

Read the clues below. Write the answers in the blanks. Choose from the words in the box.

January	April	July	October
February	May	August	November
March	June	September	December

1. First Clue: The first letter is J.
   Second Clue: The fourth day is a big holiday.

   The mystery month is _____ .

2. First Clue: The first letter is A.
   Second Clue: There are six letters in its name.

   The mystery month is _____ .

3. First Clue: This month may remind you of trees and holly.
   Second Clue: This is the last month of the year.

   The mystery month is _____ .

4. First Clue: On the first day, be ready for jokes.
   Second Clue: There are five letters in its name.

   The mystery month is _____ .

5. First Clue: This is the shortest month.
   Second Clue: Valentine's Day is in this month.

   The mystery month is _____ .

6. First Clue: The first letter is O.
   Second Clue: Halloween is in this month.

   The mystery month is _____ .

Reading Power Plus, © 1986 David S. Lake Publishers

Skill: using context clues

Sounds Puzzle

Say each sound. Circle the name of the thing that makes that sound.

1. **buzz**

   chicken   goat   bee

2. **chirp**

   tiger   bird   antelope

3. **oink**

   lion   pig   doorbell

4. **woof**

   leopard   dog   pig

5. **boom**

   thunder   candle   lamp

6. **hiss**

   puppy   telephone   snake

7. **meow**

   cat   dog   elephant

8. **vroom**

   door   shoe   motorcycle

9. **beep**

   glass   paper   horn

Reading Power Plus, © 1986 David S. Lake Publishers

Reporter

Read the newspaper story and the questions below. Then write the answers in the blanks.

The Puppet Players will visit Brook School on Tuesday, May 11. They will perform *Winnie the Pooh* for the students there. They will do two shows. The morning show will be for the lower grades, and the afternoon show will be for the higher grades.

All shows will be held in the school auditorium. They will be free of charge. Parents are welcome.

---

1. Who will be visiting Brook School?

_____

2. When will they visit? _____

3. What will they do?

_____

4. How many shows will they do? _____

5. Where will the shows be held?

_____

6. How much will it cost to see the show? _____

7. Who will go to the morning show?

_____

8. Who will go to the afternoon show?

_____

9. Are parents allowed to go? _____

Reading Power Plus, © 1986 David S. Lake Publishers

Skill: finding factual information

Odd One

In each box, draw an X on the picture that does not belong. Then, on the umbrella, find the name of the place where each group is usually found. Write the answer in the blank.

1. owl   chair

   desk   dresser

   _____

2. duck   hen

   cow   igloo

   _____

3. lion   clock

   tiger   elephant

   _____

4. grapes   cherries

   hat   lollipop

   _____

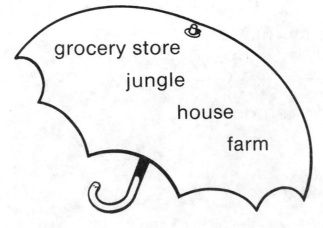

grocery store

jungle

house

farm

Reading Power Plus, © 1986 David S. Lake Publishers

Sentence and Picture

Read each sentence. Choose the correct picture. Write the letter in the blank.

1. We read from it. _____

2. It helps birds fly. _____

3. It gives us light. _____

4. You wear it on your finger. _____

5. It wakes you in the morning. _____

6. It grows on a tree. _____

A.

B.

C.

D.

E.

F.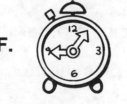

Skill: interpreting picture clues

Where's My Mother?

Write the names of the mothers in the blanks below. Use the pictures if you need help.

Babies   **Mothers**

1. A cub's mother is a _____ .

2. A duckling's mother is a _____ .

3. A kitten's mother is a _____ .

4. A calf's mother is a _____ .

5. A fawn's mother is a _____ .

6. A chick's mother is a _____ .

7. A puppy's mother is a _____ .

8. A lamb's mother is a _____ .

Skill: interpreting picture clues

46

Reading Power Plus, © 1986 David S. Lake Publishers

Mystery Word

Follow the directions.

1. Circle the letter before the first vowel.   b a c o n

2. Circle the first vowel.   a p p l e

3. Circle the third letter.   l a k e

4. Circle the second vowel.   s t a t e

5. Circle the fourth letter.   f u r r y

6. Circle the last letter.   h o n e y

7. Write the circled letters in order in the blanks below.

___ ___ ___ ___ ___ ___

Use the space below to draw a picture of the mystery word.

Skill: following directions

Do As I Say!

Follow the directions.

1. Draw a straight line (————) from the cat to the mouse.

2. Draw a zigzag line (〰) from the dog to the rabbit.

3. Draw a broken line (--------) from the little elf to the big elf.

4. Draw a curvy line (〜) from the clown to the bird.

5. Draw a dotted line (· · · · ·) from the clown to the monkey.

cat	dog	rabbit
mouse	little elf	bird
clown	monkey	big elf

Reading Power Plus, © 1986 David S. Lake Publishers

Shape Up!

Find the shape that is described by the sentence. Write its letter in the blank.

1. This shape has one straight (———) side and one curved (⌒) side. _____

2. This shape is round like a nickel. _____

3. This shape has three straight sides and no curved sides. _____

4. This shape has three straight sides and one curved side. _____

5. This shape has two straight sides and one curved side. _____

6. This shape has two straight sides and two curved sides. _____

A.	B.	C.
D.	E.	F.

Reading Power Plus, © 1986 David S. Lake Publishers

Skill: following directions

Drawing Boxes

Follow the directions.

1. In the space, draw a large box
   and write the letter A in one
   corner of it. Inside Box A, draw
   a smaller box and write the
   letter B in one corner of it.
   Inside Box B, draw an even
   smaller box. Write the letter C
   in the center of it.

2. In the space, draw a large X.
   Around the X, draw a box
   whose corners touch the ends
   of the X. Draw stripes in the
   top and bottom triangles. Draw
   dots in the two side triangles.

3. In the space, draw a circle.
   Inside the circle, draw a small
   box. Draw a dot inside the box.
   Lightly shade in the box.

Reading Power Plus, © 1986 David S. Lake Publishers

What's the Order?

If the sentences are in the correct order, draw an **X** in the **YES** column. If they are not in the correct order, draw an **X** in the **NO** column.

	Yes	No
1. Uncle Raccoon ate the candy. Uncle Raccoon bought some candy.		
2. Grandma Possum planted some vegetable seeds. Grandma Possum picked fresh vegetables from her garden.		
3. Mrs. Fox made a cake for the party. Mrs. Fox's friends came to the party.		
4. Grandpa Pig went to the door to see who was there. Grandpa Pig heard a knock at the door.		
5. Mr. Fox ate some grapes. Mr. Fox was very hungry.		
6. Mrs. Kangaroo took the bus downtown. Mrs. Kangaroo decided to go shopping.		

Reading Power Plus, © 1986 David S. Lake Publishers

Skill: understanding sequence

Riddle Fun

Read each riddle. Write the name of the pet in the blank. Choose from the names in the box.

1. I wag my tail.

   I like bones.

   I bark.

   What am I? _____

2. I am not big.

   I do not like cats.

   I love cheese.

   What am I? _____

3. I have no legs.

   My skin has scales.

   I shed my skin.

   What am I? _____

4. I make no sound.

   I have no legs.

   I live in water.

   What am I? _____

5. I have four legs.

   I have fur.

   I make a purring sound.

   What am I? _____

6. I have wings.

   I fly here and there.

   I like to sing.

   What am I? _____

dog	mouse	bird
cat	fish	snake

Reading Power Plus, © 1986 David S. Lake Publishers

That's the Difference!

Look at the pictures in each box. Draw an **X** on the picture that is different.

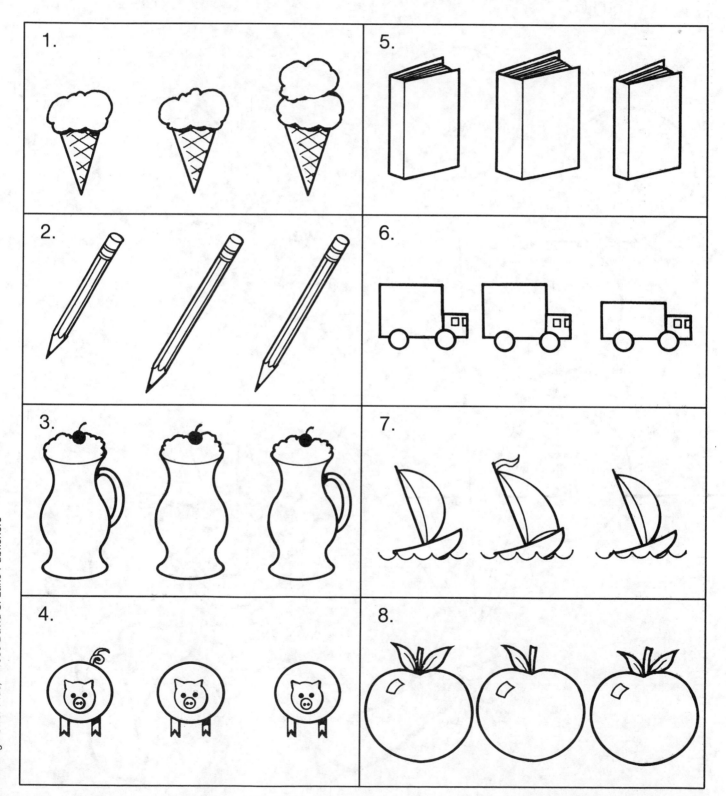

1.

2.

3.

4.

5.

6.

7.

8.

Skill: visual discrimination

Circus Time!

Find the balloons that have the same word printed twice. Color
them red. Color the other balloons blue. Color the clown any way
you like.

Skill: visual discrimination

Flying High!

Find the balloons that have the same letters on them. Color those balloons blue and red. Color the other balloons green and yellow.

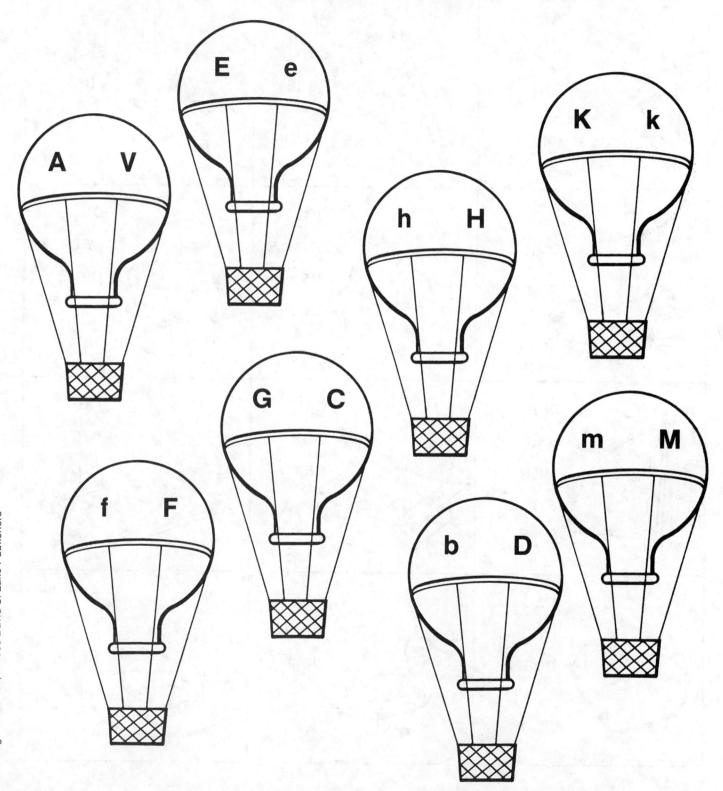

Skill: recognizing capital and lowercase letters

Picture Puzzle

Circle the word that names the picture in each box.

bad bow dog	cat card cane	star stop stick
big dog did	house mouse make	pit pat pail
sail sat sink	bat box dish	rat rug rope
had hug heart	back duck dart	hat hog hand

Sound Off!

Say the name of each picture. Circle the letter of the beginning sound.

1.		p w	7.	s d
2.		v z	8.	s t
3.		l b	9.	n t
4.		n f	10.	h b
5.		d c	11.	r f
6.		g n	12.	l w

Skill: recognizing beginning consonants

What's My Name?

Say the name of each picture. Write the letter of its beginning sound in the correct blank.

1. _____
2. _____
3. _____
4. _____
5. _____
6. _____
7. _____
8. _____

Reading Power Plus, © 1986 David S. Lake Publishers

Digraph Delights

Read each word and look at the picture. Name each picture by changing the first letter of the word to one of the digraphs in the boxes below. Then write the name of the picture in the blank.

1. tip _____

2. dirty **30** _____

3. feel _____

4. peep _____

5. power _____

6. ferry _____

7. bell _____

8. deck ✓ _____

9. dumb _____

10. wild _____

th	sh	wh	ch

Reading Power Plus, © 1986 David S. Lake Publishers

Skill: **using digraphs**

Hear the Ending

Say the name of each picture. Circle the letter of the ending sound.

1.		t m
2.		g p
3.		r g
4.		x m
5.		p k
6.		j n
7.		l z
8.		t p
9.		b d
10.		f r

Reading Power Plus, © 1986 David S. Lake Publishers

Two Together

Draw a line from the word in the circle to each word in the list that will make a compound word. Write the compound words in the blanks.

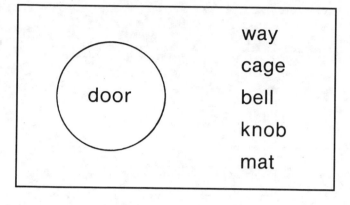

way
cage
bell
knob
mat

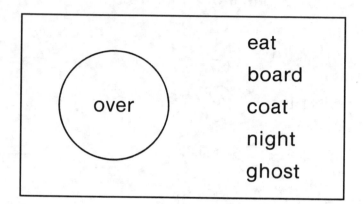

eat
board
coat
night
ghost

1. _____

2. _____

3. _____

4. _____

5. _____

6. _____

7. _____

8. _____

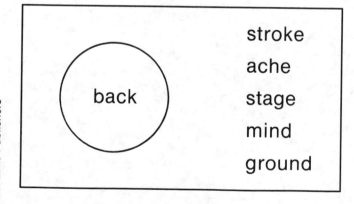

stroke
ache
stage
mind
ground

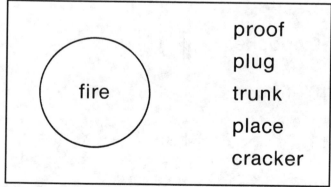

proof
plug
trunk
place
cracker

9. _____

10. _____

11. _____

12. _____

13. _____

14. _____

15. _____

16. _____

Skill: recognizing compound words

Add Them Up

Make a compound word by joining the name of the picture and the short word. Write the compound word in the blank. Use the clues at the bottom of the page when you do not know how to spell the name of a picture.

1. rain + = _____

2. blue + = _____

3. + box = _____

4. + cake = _____

5. sand + = _____

6. hair + = _____

7. + sauce = _____

8. + light = _____

9. pocket + = _____

10. finger + = _____

11. + ball = _____

12. + brow = _____

Clues

bow	cup	star	nail
brush	mail	book	eye
apple	bird	foot	box

Reading Power Plus, © 1986 David S. Lake Publishers

Do-It-Yourself Words

Draw lines from the words in Column A to the words in Column B to make compound words. Write the compound words in the blanks to complete the sentences.

A	B
land	stand
soap	lace
neck	scape
grand	suds

1. What a lovely _____ you are wearing!

2. My tub overflowed with _____ .

3. The _____ around the mansion was beautiful.

4. We sat in the _____ .

A	B
fan	lash
whip	fare
drift	cast
out	wood

5. A _____ was played on trumpets.

6. John suffered _____ from the accident.

7. The _____ had no home.

8. Gloria saw two pieces of _____ on the water.

A	B
land	slide
slap	scraper
sky	stick
spy	glass

9. The _____ seemed to touch the clouds.

10. A clown uses _____ comedy to make the audience laugh.

11. Frank won by a _____ .

12. Looking through the _____ , the sailor saw a small ship.

Skill: recognizing compound words

Getting Bigger, Getting Smaller

Draw a line from each contraction to the two words it stands for.

1. I'll	will not
2. we've	you will
3. you'll	I will
4. won't	he is
5. he's	we have
6. they're	who is
7. don't	they are
8. who's	do not

Draw a line from each pair of words to the correct contraction.

9. could not	mustn't
10. should not	shouldn't
11. I have	she'll
12. must not	I've
13. she will	doesn't
14. you are	couldn't
15. it is	it's
16. does not	you're

Skill: recognizing contractions

Reading Power Plus, © 1986 David S. Lake Publishers

Shrinking Words

Draw a line under the two words in each sentence that could be made into a contraction. Write the contraction in the blank.

1. I have found the missing key. _____

2. Emma was not tired after running. _____

3. I know you have told your mother. _____

4. You need not buy me a present. _____

5. They will save us a piece of cake. _____

6. Mark will not eat his dinner. _____

7. Sorry, but you are too late to see the movie. _____

8. That is a good picture of you. _____

9. Those are not my socks. _____

10. It has not rained in three weeks. _____

Skill: recognizing contractions

What's My Line?

Draw a line from each word to the correct picture.

small smaller smallest		tall taller tallest	
fat fatter fattest		wide wider widest	
long longer longest		short shorter shortest	
big bigger biggest		thin thinner thinnest	

Skill: using comparisons

80

Vowel Hunt

Two words in each row have the same vowel sound as the picture.
Circle them.

1.		trot	toad	poke
2.		hut	mule	jut
3.		cake	cat	frame
4.		bed	seat	feet
5.		light	string	wing
6.		dart	bat	mark
7.		huge	hug	dust
8.		cow	snow	flower

Reading Power Plus, © 1986 David S. Lake Publishers

Skill: recognizing vowel sounds

Rolling Along

Circle the words on each cart that have the vowel sound shown on the handle.

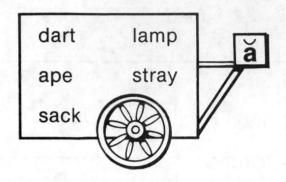

dart   lamp

ape   stray

sack

ă

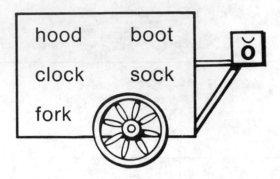

hood   boot

clock   sock

fork

ŏ

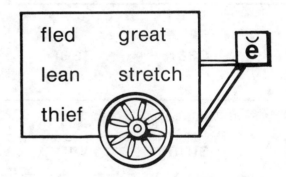

fled   great

lean   stretch

thief

ĕ

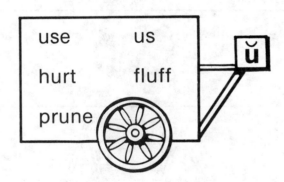

use   us

hurt   fluff

prune

ŭ

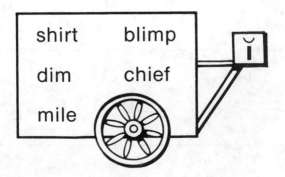

shirt   blimp

dim   chief

mile

ĭ

Reading Power Plus, © 1986 David S. Lake Publishers

Batter Up!

Read each word in the lineup. Strike out the silent **e** if a real word would remain. Write the new word in the batter's box. The first one has been done for you.

Lineup	**Batter's Box**	**Lineup**	**Batter's Box**
1. face	_____	11. note	_____
2. tube	tub	12. grape	_____
3. plume	_____	13. cute	_____
4. gave	_____	14. clothe	_____
5. joke	_____	15. use	_____
6. slide	_____	16. mule	_____
7. tone	_____	17. name	_____
8. line	_____	18. pride	_____
9. mate	_____	19. dime	_____
10. dive	_____	20. globe	_____

Skill: recognizing vowel sounds

Solve the O Case

Read each clue and write the answer in the puzzle. Words that go **across** have the **long o** sound. Words that go **down** have the **short o** sound. Use the word file if you need help.

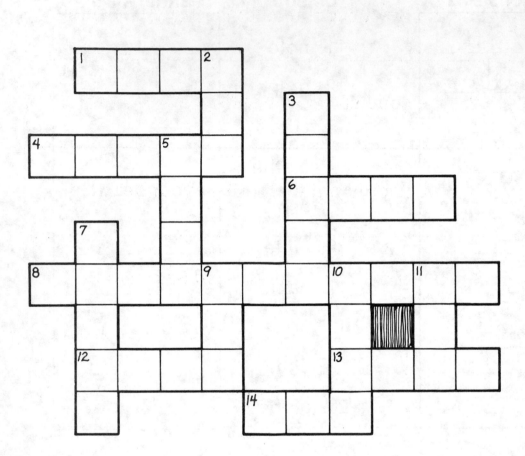

Word File

old

hot

ghost

soap

spot

not

pot

pond

cold

coat

rocks

clothespins

clock

note

ACROSS

1 You wash with it.
4 A Halloween sight
6 Opposite of **hot**
8 They go with clotheslines.
12 It keeps you warm.
13 A short letter
14 Opposite of **new**

DOWN

2 You cook in it.
3 Big stones
5 A stain or mark
7 It tells time.
9 Opposite of **cold**
10 A small lake
11 It rhymes with **cot**.

Skill: recognizing vowel sounds

84

Reading Power Plus, © 1986 David S. Lake Publishers

Hear, Hear!

Read each key word. Underline three words in the sentence that have the same vowel sound as the key word.

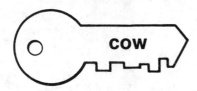 1. The boy used three coins to buy a new toy.

 2. The soup spoon is beside the blue bowl.

 3. You should put the book in your desk.

 4. The snow plow was so loud Sara had to shout.

 5. The herd of thirty cattle returned safely.

6. The old man slowly followed the crowd.

7. Fall, sometimes called autumn, is my favorite season.

8. The dog stared into the darkness, then started to bark.

Skill: recognizing vowel sounds

Skyscrapers

Read the words on the buildings. Find 1 one-syllable word, 2 two-syllable words, 3 three-syllable words, and 4 four-syllable words. Write the words in the correct garages.

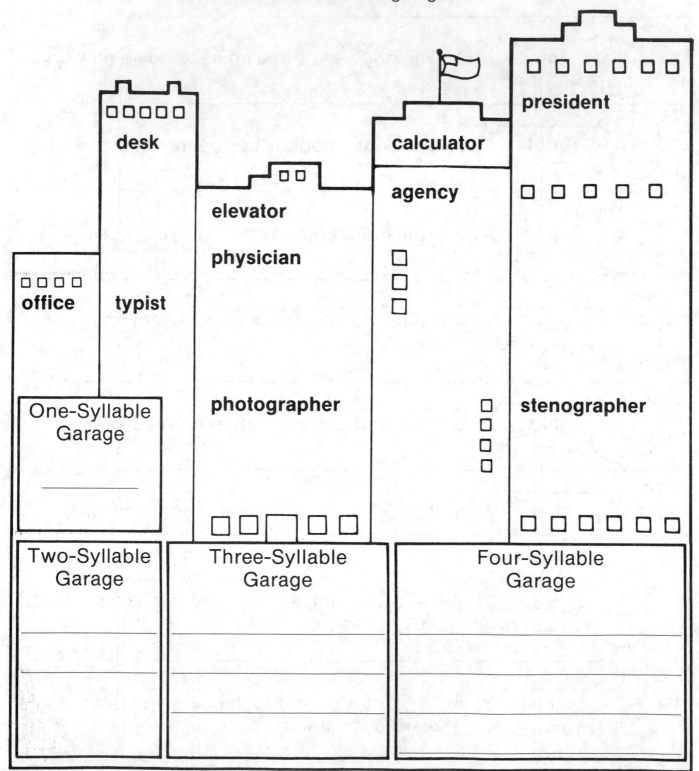

desk

president

calculator

agency

elevator

physician

office

typist

One-Syllable
Garage

_____

photographer

stenographer

Two-Syllable
Garage

_____

_____

Three-Syllable
Garage

_____

_____

Four-Syllable
Garage

_____

_____

_____

Reading Power Plus, © 1986 David S. Lake Publishers

Stop, Look, and Listen!

Read each word and listen for the syllables. Write the number of syllables in the traffic light next to the word. The first one has been done for you.

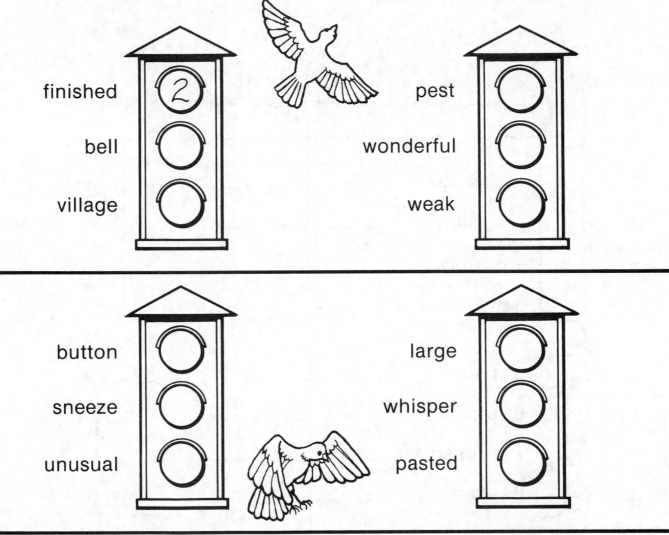

finished   2

bell

village

pest

wonderful

weak

button

sneeze

unusual

large

whisper

pasted

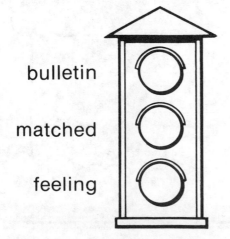

bulletin

matched

feeling

spatter

beads

shadow

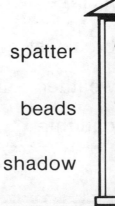

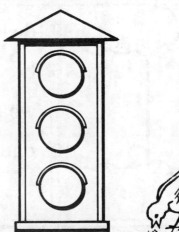

Skill: recognizing syllables

Reading Power Plus, © 1986 David S. Lake Publishers

Slice It

Divide each word by drawing a line between the syllables. Write
the syllables in the blanks. The first one has been done for you.
Use a dictionary if you need help.

1. seven   sev   en
2. afford   _____ _____
3. music   _____ _____
4. furry   _____ _____

5. paper   _____
6. picnic   _____
7. broken   _____
8. scatter _____

9. divide   _____
10. breakfast _____
11. weather   _____
12. daughter _____

Reading Power Plus, © 1986 David S. Lake Publishers

File It

Arrange the words from **A** to **Z**. Write them, in order, in the blanks.
There is one word for each letter of the alphabet.

grandmother	radio	x-ray	nothing
brook	something	umbrella	other
like	help	farmer	place
maybe	jacket	carbon	wagon
alligator	donkey	either	quiet
zebra	telephone	island	
yard	vest	knit	

1. _____
2. _____
3. _____
4. _____
5. _____
6. _____
7. _____
8. _____
9. _____
10. _____
11. _____
12. _____
13. _____

14. _____
15. _____
16. _____
17. _____
18. _____
19. _____
20. _____
21. _____
22. _____
23. _____
24. _____
25. _____
26. _____

Skill: using alphabetical order

On the Track

Read the words on each set of railroad tracks. Write them in correct alphabetical order on each railroad car.

C Train
1. _____
2. _____
3. _____

core   cake   chair

D Train
1. _____
2. _____
3. _____

deer   door   dress

K Train
1. _____
2. _____
3. _____

kite   kit   knee

S Train
1. _____
2. _____
3. _____

string   sure   soon

L Train
1. _____
2. _____
3. _____

letter   laugh   lost

P Train
1. _____
2. _____
3. _____

pencil   plant   pack

Skill: using alphabetical order

Pieces of Pizza

Read each prefix. Choose two words from the pizza that can go with the prefix. Write the words in the blanks. Shade in the pieces of pizza that you used. The first one has been done for you.

1. dis _order_

   dis _____

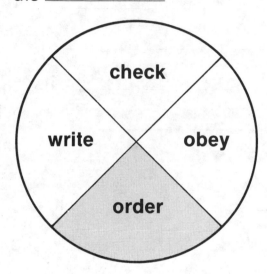

2. pre _____

   pre _____

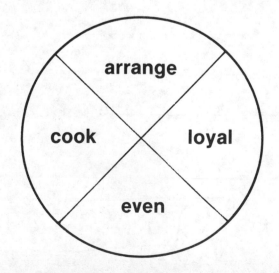

3. in _____

   in _____

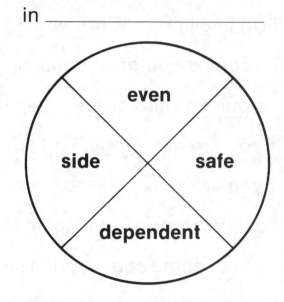

4. mis _____

   mis _____

Skill: using prefixes

Undoing and Redoing

Add **un** or **re** to the underlined word to complete each sentence. Write the new word in the blank. The first one has been done for you.

1. To <u>decorate</u> a room again is to ____redecorate____ it.

2. If you put the <u>cap</u> back on a bottle, you _____ it.

3. Two lines that are not <u>equal</u> are _____ .

4. To <u>copy</u> a composition again is to _____ it.

5. To <u>build</u> a sand castle again is to _____ it.

6. If you are not <u>happy</u>, you are _____ .

7. If you are not <u>able</u> to ski, you are _____ .

8. To <u>read</u> a good book again is to _____ it.

9. To <u>heat</u> some soup again is to _____ it.

10. Something that is not <u>necessary</u> is _____ .

11. A person who is not <u>employed</u> is _____ .

12. When an area is <u>developed</u> again, it is _____ .

13. When airplanes get more <u>fuel</u>, they _____ .

14. A room that is not <u>tidy</u> is _____ .

15. If you <u>pay</u> back a loan, you _____ it.

Reading Power Plus, © 1986 David S. Lake Publishers

Answer Key

Animal Crackers, page 1

Countdown, page 2

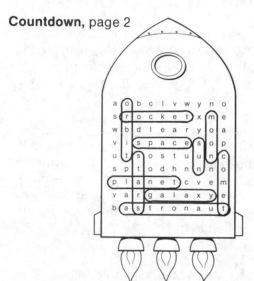

The answers may be written in any order: orbit, stars or star, moon, rocket, space, planet, galaxy, astronaut, comet, sun.

What's in a Word? page 3

1. plan or lane, 2. row, 3. how or owl, 4. car or art, 5. tar, 6. hot, 7. one, 8. rack, 9. pool, 10. low, 11. loud, 12. monk or key, 13. past, 14. car, 15. ant, 16. rain, 17. oil, 18. oat or oats or float, 19. poke, 20. was

Which Is Which? page 4

1. hear, 2. our, 3. pear, 4. stare, 5. see, 6. knew, 7. due, 8. hoarse, 9. fir, 10. seam, 11. too, 12. bee, 13. hair, 14. days, 15. wring

A Pair of Pears, page 5

1. two, a. too, 2. son, b. sun, 3. hare, c. hair, 4. blue, d. blew, 5. tail, e. tale, 6. flour, f. flower

Food for Thought, page 6

1. onions, 2. soup, 3. grapes, 4. chicken, 5. bread, 6. milk, 7. potatoes, 8. turkey, 9. pickles, 10. cheese, 11. peanuts, 12. supermarket

Make the Connection, page 7

1. sold, 2. hot, 3. foot, 4. not, 5. nest, 6. large, 7. row, 8. tick

Match Maker, page 8

1. a place to keep animals, 2. an instrument used for writing, 3. to choose, 4. a tool used for breaking soil, 5. to keep oneself back, 6. a verse repeated in music, 7. to expel air from the mouth, 8. a sudden hard stroke or hit

Look-Alikes, page 9

1. a, 2. b, 3. b, 4. a, 5. b, 6. a, 7. b, 8. a, 9. a, 10. b

Double Trouble, page 10

1. b, a, 2. b, a, 3. a, b, 4. b, a, 5. b, a, 6. a, b, 7. b, a

Two by Two, page 11

1. pig, hog, 2. bubble, fizz, 3. piece, part, 4. easy, simple, 5. near, close, 6. path, trail, 7. leap, jump, 8. rope, cord, 9. large, big, 10. sob, cry, 11. penny, cent, 12. fold, bend, 13. sew, mend, 14. plate, dish

What Do You Mean? page 12

1. unusual, 2. exact, 3. complains, 4. offensive, 5. punished, 6. trip, 7. empty, 8. wise, 9. prize, 10. fix

Opposites Attract, page 13

1. young, 2. strong, 3. in, 4. well, 5. night, 6. light, 7. loose, 8. back, 9. sweet, 10. bright, 11. empty, 12. fast, 13. bottom, 14. shallow, 15. found, 16. before

Look the Opposite Way, page 14

1. leave, 2. tame, 3. reject, 4. tidy, 5. cruel, 6. unfriendly, 7. plentiful, 8. fair

Pay Attention! page 15
1. O, 2. S, 3. O, 4. O, 5. O, 6. O, 7. O, 8. S,
9. O, 10. S, 11. S, 12. S, 13. O, 14. O, 15. S,
16. O, 17. O, 18. S, 19. S, 20. S

Not All the Same, page 16
1. opposite, 2. same, 3. same, 4. opposite,
5. opposite, 6. same, 7. same

Pick and Choose, page 17
1. smell, sniff, 2. flowers, weeds, 3. eggs, chicks,
4. taxi, truck, 5. bread, cookies, 6. read, spell,
7. nine, seven, 8. pet, dog

Picnic Puzzle, page 18

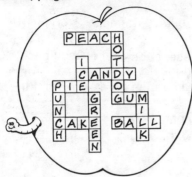

What Does It Mean? page 19
The following sentences should be underlined:
1. It overturns. 2. He is grouchy. 3. It falls in.
4. It breaks. 5. It gets bigger. 6. It is not to be
used. 7. She feels awkward. 8. It rots.

Easy As A, B, C, page 20
1. b, 2. c, 3. a, 4. c, 5. a, 6. c, 7. b, 8. c

A Picture Story, page 21
The words should appear in the following order:
cake, eggs, milk, bowl, oven, candles

Gone to Market, page 22
1. to the market, 2. eggs, cereal, and milk, 3. at
the counter, 4. walked, 5. near her house, 6. the
next day

Aunt Mary's Restaurant, page 23
1. restaurant, 2. city, 3. apple, 4. pies, 5. busy

Word Play, page 24
1. seven, 2. salmon, 3. upstream, 4. August,
5. small, 6. pink, 7. swiftly

Sentence Sense, Page 25
1. sky, 2. ground, 3. wheels, 4. cold, 5. dessert,
6. cows, 7. newspaper, 8. loud, 9. chocolate,
10. peanuts, 11. summer, 12. stream

Word Choice, page 26
1. rake, 2. come, 3. sun, 4. sell, 5. stop, 6. pan,
7. saw, 8. three, 9. here, 10. lake, 11. pet,
12. horse

Mystery Months, page 27
1. July, 2. August, 3. December, 4. April,
5. February, 6. October

Sounds Puzzle, page 28
1. bee, 2. bird, 3. pig, 4. dog, 5. thunder,
6. snake, 7. cat, 8. motorcycle, 9. horn

Reporter, page 29
1. the Puppet Players, 2. Tuesday, May 11,
3. perform *Winnie the Pooh,* 4. two, 5. in the
school auditorium, 6. nothing, 7. the lower
grades, 8. the higher grades, 9. yes

Odd One, page 30
1. An X should be drawn on the owl, and *house*
should be written in the blank. 2. An X should be
drawn on the igloo, and *farm* should be written in
the blank. 3. An X should be drawn on the clock,
and *jungle* should be written in the blank. 4. An
X should be drawn on the hat, and *grocery store*
should be written in the blank.

Find It, page 31
The following words should be underlined:
1. coat, hat, 2. bird, airplane, 3. snowball, ice,
4. apple, pear, 5. lamp, sun, 6. map, book,
7. bicycle, car, 8. woman, bird, 9. fruit, fish,
10. grass, chair, 11. music, noise, 12. cherry,
apple

Which Words Do Not Belong? page 32
The following words should be underlined:
1. short, 2. flag, 3. street, 4. gift, 5. tight,
6. pony, 7. puppy, 8. soap, 9. feather, 10. white,
11. smell, 12. sing, 13. pencil, 14. alphabet,
15. lunch

Persons, Places, and Things, page 33
1. T, 2. T, 3. P, 4. P, 5. T, 6. T, 7. P, 8. T, 9. T,
10. T, 11. T, 12. T, 13. T, 14. T, 15. T, 16. T,
17. T, 18. P, 19. T, 20. T

Circle It, page 34
The following words should be circled:
1. window, 2. bushel, 3. book, 4. salty, 5. blossom, 6. Monday, 7. nurse, 8. soda, 9. heap, 10. dust, 11. glass, 12. ruler, 13. soft, 14. play, 15. skip

Where Would You Look? page 35
1. desk, 2. kitchen, 3. restaurant, 4. library, 5. bakery, 6. baseball field, 7. garden

Right Words, page 36
The following words should be underlined:
1. green, pink, red, yellow, 2. song, melody, tune, beat, 3. bear, dog, kangaroo, deer, 4. leaves, roots, trunk, branches, 5. mother, aunt, lawyer, uncle, 6. coat, shirt, gloves, blouse, 7. peach, pear, plum, orange, tangerine, 8. stars, moon, lights

Find the Idea, page 37
1. C, 2. B, 3. A, 4. E, 5. D

Pick a Good Title, page 38
first paragraph: The First Airplane Ride
second paragraph: A Rainy Saturday
third paragraph: A New Sled
fourth paragraph: Some New Friends

Finding Out, page 39
1. where, 2. who, 3. when, 4. when, 5. what, 6. where, 7. who, 8. when, 9. what, 10. where, 11. what, 12. where

Scrambled Sentences, page 40
1. Alex will go to the store. 2. An apple fell from the tree. 3. It was a funny movie. 4. Elephants like to eat peanuts. 5. It started to rain just as we were leaving. 6. Bonnie likes this kind of music. 7. Where do you think Alice is? 8. Help me look for my shoe.
Note: Answers may vary slightly—accept any arrangement that makes sense.

Boxed In, page 41
1. The bird flew from the tree. 2. What crops have the farmers grown this year? 3. Why do you want to go there? 4. The sun shone brightly through my window. 5. I'm going to visit my cousin in Chicago. 6. Amy will visit Asia next month. 7. You must know the answer to that question. 8. You now must answer that question.
Note: Answers may vary slightly—accept any arrangement that makes sense.

Pick the Picture, page 42
1. D, 2. A, 3. E, 4. C, 5. B, 6. A, 7. D, 8. B

Which One? page 43

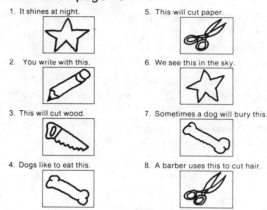

Tell Me, Please, page 44

Sentence and Picture, page 45
1. B, 2. D, 3. E, 4. C, 5. F, 6. A

Where's My Mother? page 46
1. bear, 2. duck, 3. cat, 4. cow, 5. deer, 6. hen, 7. dog, 8. sheep

To Tell the Truth, page 47
1. F, 2. T, 3. T, 4. T, 5. T, 6. F, 7. T, 8. F, 9. F, 10. F
The following words should be written above the underlined words in the sentences marked **F**:
1. run, 6. cow, 8. child, 9. fruits, 10. hot

True or False? page 48

1. A dog is an animal. 2. A cat can purr. 3. A cat has claws. 4. An apple grows on a tree. 5. A dog has fur.

Note: The sentences may be written in any order.

Choose What's True, page 49

1. nests, 2. Leaves, 3. fly, 4. hop, 5. eggs, 6. jungles, 7. clock, 8. Cats, 9. lights, 10. letter, 11. sister, 12. key, 13. brush, 14. green, 15. gold

What's the Answer? page 50

1. Yes, 2. Yes, 3. Yes, 4. No, 5. No, 6. No, 7. Yes, 8. No, 9. Yes, 10. Yes, 11. Yes, 12. No, 13. No, 14. No, 15. Yes

Mystery Word, page 51

For questions 1–6, the following letters should be circled:

1. b, 2. a, 3. k, 4. e, 5. r, 6. y; 7. b a k e r y

Do As I Say! page 52

Shape Up! page 53

1. F, 2. B, 3. E, 4. D, 5. C, 6. A

Drawing Boxes, page 54

 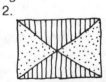 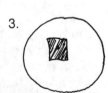

Note: Illustrations may vary. Accept any illustration that fulfills the requirements.

Different Things to Do, page 55

1. Draw an X on the circle.

2. Draw a line under the last letter of the word below.

m a s <u>t</u>

3. Draw a circle around the two letters that are the same in the word below.

c o o k

4. Shade in all the squares.

5. Shade in the left side of the butterfly lightly. Shade in the right side of the butterfly heavily. Draw stripes on the middle part of the butterfly.

6. Draw a circle around each vowel in the word below.

i n s u r a n c e

7. Draw a large triangle and a small square.

8. Draw a line under the first syllable of the word below.

<u>r i p</u> p l e

One, Two, Three, page 56

A. 2, 1, 3; B. 2, 3, 1; C. 3, 2, 1; D. 2, 3, 1; E. 1, 3, 2

What's the Order? page 57

1. The X should be in the NO column.
2. The X should be in the YES column.
3. The X should be in the YES column.
4. The X should be in the NO column.
5. The X should be in the NO column.
6. The X should be in the NO column.

Riddle Fun, page 58

1. dog, 2. mouse, 3. snake, 4. fish, 5. cat, 6. bird

Guess the Riddle, page 59

1. duck, 2. fish, 3. tree, 4. cow, 5. candle

Lost and Found, page 60

The following words should be underlined:

1. books, 2. books, 3. sweaters, 4. glasses, 5. five

That's the Difference! page 61

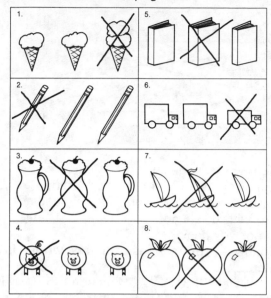

Circus Time! page 62

The balloons with the following words printed twice should be colored red: *to, we, fire, not.*

Flying High! page 63

The balloons with the following sets of letters should be colored blue and red: *f F, m M, E e, h H, K k.*

Picture Puzzle, page 64

Sound Off! page 65

The following letters should be circled:
1. p, 2. v, 3. l, 4. f, 5. c, 6. n, 7. d, 8. s, 9. t,
10. b, 11. r, 12. w

What's My Name? page 66

1. n, 2. b, 3. l, 4. d, 5. b, 6. s, 7. r or b, 8. m

Digraph Delights, page 67

1. whip, 2. thirty, 3. wheel, 4. sheep, 5. shower,
6. cherry, 7. shell, 8. check, 9. thumb, 10. child

Hear the Ending, page 68

The following letters should be circled:
1. t, 2. p, 3. g, 4. x, 5. k, 6. n, 7. l, 8. p, 9. b,
10. f

Choose an Ending, page 69

1. hard, 2. sharp, 3. cot, 4. worm, 5. cup,
6. band, 7. map, 8. chin, 9. book

Pick a Blend, page 70

1. cr, 2. gr, 3. gl, 4. st, 5. br, 6. fl, 7. tr, 8. cl,
9. fr, 10. dr, 11. bl, 12. sp

Silly Sentences, page 71

1. sleep, 2. price, 3. free, 4. broke, 5. crib, 6.
trade, 7. snake, 8. sweet, 9. flag, 10. dragon's

At Times They Rhyme, page 72

The following words should be circled:
1. Yes, 2. Yes, 3. No, 4. Yes, 5. No, 6. Yes,
7. Yes, 8. No

Rhyme Time, page 73

The answers should appear in the following
order:
1. tell, bell, 2. bone, cone, 3. soon, noon, 4.
sack, back, 5. pick, wick, 6. cane, pane, 7. fill,
dill, 8. camp, damp

Three in a Row, page 74

1. now, cow, 2. bat, fat, 3. tall, wall, 4. rug, bug,
5. win, fin, 6. mine, line, 7. dish, fish, 8. look,
book, 9. wig, pig, 10. bad, sad, 11. hose, nose,
12. name, tame, 13. cold, fold, 14. tag, wag

Two Together, page 75

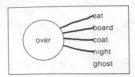

doorway
doorbell
doorknob
doormat

overeat
overboard
overcoat
overnight

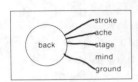

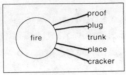

backstroke
backache
backstage
background

fireproof
fireplug
fireplace
firecracker

Add Them Up, page 76
1. rainbow, 2. bluebird, 3. mailbox, 4. cupcake, 5. sandbox, 6. hairbrush, 7. applesauce, 8. starlight, 9. pocketbook, 10. fingernail, 11. football, 12. eyebrow

Do-It-Yourself Words, page 77

1. necklace, 2. soapsuds, 3. landscape, 4. grandstand, 5. fanfare, 6. whiplash, 7. outcast, 8. driftwood, 9. skyscraper, 10. slapstick, 11. landslide, 12. spyglass

Getting Bigger, Getting Smaller, page 78

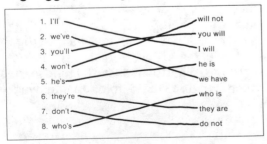

(Getting Bigger, Getting Smaller continued)

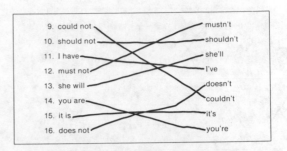

Shrinking Words, page 79
The following words should be underlined:
1. I have, 2. was not, 3. you have, 4. need not, 5. They will, 6. will not, 7. you are, 8. That is, 9. are not, 10. has not
The following contractions should be written in the blanks:
1. I've, 2. wasn't, 3. you've, 4. needn't, 5. They'll, 6. won't, 7. you're, 8. That's, 9. aren't, 10. hasn't

What's My Line? page 80

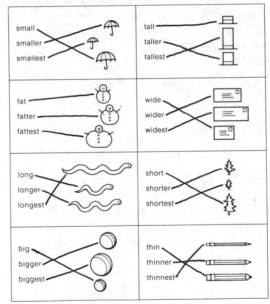

Vowel Hunt, page 81
The following words should be circled:
1. toad, poke, 2. hut, jut, 3. cake, frame, 4. seat, feet, 5. string, wing, 6. dart, mark, 7. hug, dust, 8. cow, flower

Rolling Along, page 82

The cart marked ă should have *lamp* and *sack* circled. The cart marked ĕ should have *stretch* and *fled* circled. The cart marked ĭ should have *blimp* and *dim* circled. The cart marked ŏ should have *sock* and *clock* circled. The cart marked ŭ should have *fluff* and *us* circled.

Batter Up! page 83

Lineup	Batter's Box	Lineup	Batter's Box
1. face		11. note	not
2. tube	tub	12. grape	
3. plume	plum	13. cute	cut
4. gave		14. clothe	cloth
5. joke		15. use	us
6. slide	slid	16. mule	
7. tone	ton	17. name	
8. line		18. pride	
9. mate	mat	19. dime	dim
10. dive		20. globe	glob

Solve the O Case, page 84

A crossword with: SOAP, GHOST, ROOK, COLD, COOK, CLOTHESPINS, COAT, NOTE, OLD, COOK (down).

Hear, Hear! page 85

The following words should be underlined:
1. boy, coins, toy, 2. soup, spoon, blue, 3. should, put, book, 4. plow, loud, shout, 5. herd, thirty, returned, 6. old, slowly, followed, 7. Fall, called, autumn, 8. darkness, started, bark

Skyscrapers, page 86

One-Syllable Garage: desk
Two-Syllable Garage: office, typist
Three-Syllable Garage: physician, agency, president
Four-Syllable Garage: elevator, photographer, calculator, stenographer

Stop, Look, and Listen! page 87

The numbers written next to each word should be as follows:

finished—2	pest—1
bell—1	wonderful—3
village—2	weak—1
button—2	large—1
sneeze—1	whisper—2
unusual—4	pasted—2
bulletin—3	spatter—2
matched—1	beads—1
feeling—2	shadow—2

Slice It, page 88

1. seven, sev en, 2. afford, af ford, 3. music, mu sic, 4. furry, fur ry, 5. paper, pa per, 6. picnic, pic nic, 7. broken, bro ken, 8. scatter, scat ter, 9. divide, di vide, 10. breakfast, break fast, 11. weather, weath er, 12. daughter, daugh ter

File It, page 89

1. alligator, 2. brook, 3. carbon, 4. donkey, 5. either, 6. farmer, 7. grandmother, 8. help, 9. island, 10. jacket, 11. knit, 12. like, 13. maybe, 14. nothing, 15. other, 16. place, 17. quiet, 18. radio, 19. something, 20. telephone, 21. umbrella, 22. vest, 23. wagon, 24. x-ray, 25. yard, 26. zebra

On the Track, page 90

C Train: 1. cake, 2. chair, 3. core; D Train: 1. deer, 2. door, 3. dress; K Train: 1. kit, 2. kite, 3. knee; S Train: 1. soon, 2. string, 3. sure; L Train: 1. laugh, 2. letter, 3. lost; P Train: 1. pack, 2. pencil, 3. plant

Big Foot and Small Feet, page 91

1. cheeks, 2. flashes, 3. mice, 4. flies, 5. tables, 6. boys, 7. men, 8. watches, 9. knives, 10. potatoes, 11. foxes, 12. seats, 13. peaches, 14. ants, 15. sheep

One or More? page 92

The single mitten should have the following words written on it: cheese, row, painting, goose, monkey, baseball, glass, envelope, tanker.
The pair of mittens should have the following words written on them: brushes, thieves, dresses, elephants, ladies, boxes, pennies, wives, laces

Three-Base Hits, page 93

◇ lock ◇ *locked* *locking*	◇ read ◇ *reading* *reader*	◇ wish ◇ *wishful* *wished*
◇ hook ◇ *hooked* *unhook*	◇ bake ◇ *bakes* *baker*	◇ yell ◇ *yelling* *yelled*

Get to the Root of It, page 94

1. hold, 2. paint, 3. wise, 4. wind, 5. stitch, 6. clap, 7. tooth, 8. wax, 9. dream, 10. draft, 11. gentle, 12. fill, 13. warm, 14. penny, 15. taste, 16. please, 17. hobby, 18. plenty, 19. guide, 20. use

The following syllables or letters should be written on the leaves:
1. ing, 2. er, 3. un, 4. re, 5. es, 6. ping, 7. less, 8. re, es, 9. er, 10. y, 11. ness, 12. ing, 13. th, 14. iless, 15. iest, 16. dis, ing, 17. ies, 18. iful, 19. mis, d, 20. un, d

Pieces of Pizza, page 95

1. order, obey, 2. arrange, cook, 3. side, dependent, 4. understand, treat.
The pieces of pizza with these words should be shaded in.

Undoing and Redoing, page 96

1. redecorate, 2. recap, 3. unequal, 4. recopy, 5. rebuild, 6. unhappy, 7. unable, 8. reread, 9. reheat, 10. unnecessary, 11. unemployed, 12. redeveloped, 13. refuel, 14. untidy, 15. repay

Tag It, page 97

1. ful, 2. X, 3. ful, 4. X, 5. ful, 6. X, 7. less, 8. less, 9. X, 10. less, 11. y, 12. y, 13. X, 14. X, 15. y, 16. en, 17. en, 18. X, 19. X, 20. en, 21. X, 22. er, 23. er, 24. X, 25. er, 26. X, 27. ing, 28. X, 29. ing, 30. ing

Adding Endings, page 98

1. sweetly, 2. shortly, 3. hopeless, 4. cheerfully, 5. really, 6. wingless, 7. barely, 8. rudely, 9. slightly, 10. restless, 11. honestly, 12. meatless, 13. effortless, 14. certainly, 15. windowless

How Does It Sound? page 99

The bag marked *t* should have the following words written on it: talked, picked, pushed, shopped, liked, matched.
The bag marked *d* should have the following words written on it: played, sailed, closed, called.
The bag marked *ed* should have the following words written on it: sounded, pasted, started, fainted, landed.

Name That Sound, page 100

The following letters should be circled:
1. t, 2. d, 3. t, 4. ed, 5. t, 6. t, 7. ed, 8. t, 9. ed, 10. t, 11. ed, 12. d